VIKAS
LEARN TO DRAW

CARTOONS ①

(An innovative series on art education)

Artist and Visualizer
SUBODH NARVEKAR

Price : Rs. 45.00

N...........................TED

F 1211

A NOTE FROM THE PUBLISHER

Encouraged by the response to our FUN SERIES, we present yet another creative art series called, LEARN TO DRAW, the first volume being, CARTOONS.

Cartoons! The very word seems filled with a certain magic that enchants children and adults alike!

Every child has a natural affinity for learning animation, not only as a technique but as a means of self-expression as well. In this book we have tried to simplify the technique, using simple sketches and guidelines to instruct the child.

Though a great deal of emphasis has been placed on the animation of people, we have also incorporated a few pages on animals, birds and even inanimate objects which spring to life, as well as animated letters of the alphabet.

What's more, the book is loads of fun from the first page to the last!

VIKAS

LEARN TO DRAW CARTOONS–1

ISBN 978-81-243-0277-4

 **NAVNEET PUBLICATIONS (INDIA) LIMITED**

Mumbai : Bhavani Shankar Road, Dadar, Mumbai–400 028. (Tel. 6662 6565 ● Fax : 6662 6470)

www.navneet.com ● e-mail : publications@navneet.com

Ahmadabad : Navneet House, Gurukul Road, Memnagar, Ahmadabad–380 052. (Tel. 6630 5000)

Bengalooru : Sri Balaji's, No. 12, 2nd Floor, 3rd Cross, Malleswaram, Next to Hotel Halli Mane, Bengalooru–560 003. (Tel. 2346 5740)

Chennai : 30, Shriram Nagar, North Street, Alwarpet, Chennai–600 018. (Tel. 2434 6404)

Delhi : 2E / 23, Orion Plaza, 2nd & 3rd Flr., Jhandewalan Extn., New Delhi – 110 055. (Tel. 2361 0170)

Hyderabad : Kalki Plaza, Plot No. 67, Door No. 6, Krishna Puri Colony, West Maredpalley, Secunderabad–500 026. (Tel. 2780 0146)

Kolkata : 1st Floor, 7, Suren Tagore Road, Kolkata–700 019. (Tel. 2460 4178)

Nagpur : 63, Opp. Shivaji Science College, Congress Nagar, Nagpur–440 012. (Tel. 242 1522)

Nashik : Dharmaraj Plaza, Old Gangapur Naka, Gangapur Road, Nashik–422 005. (Tel. 231 0627)

Navsari : 3 / C, Arvind Nagar Society, Lunsikui Road, Navsari–396 445. (Tel. 244 186)

Patna : 205, 2nd Floor, Jagdamba Towers, Sahdeo Mahto Marg, Srikrishnapuri, Patna–800 001. (Tel. 254 0321)

Pune : Navneet Bhavan, 1302, Shukrawar Peth, Bajirao Road, Pune–411 002. (Tel. 2443 1007)

Rajkot : 20-21, Jagnath Corner, B / h Dhanrajani Building, Yagnik Road, Rajkot–360 001.

Surat : 1, Ground Floor, Shree Vallabh Complex, Kotwal Street, Nanpara, Surat–395 001. (Tel. 246 3927)

Vadodara : Near Hanuman Wadi, Sardar Bhuvan Khancho, Vadodara–390 001.

Published by Navneet Publications (India) Ltd., Dantali, Gujarat.
Printed by Printmann, 8, Adhyaru Ind. Estate, Lower Parel, Mumbai–400 013.   0919

You probably know that the height of a man is approximately 7 times that of his head.

While drawing cartoons, however, one need not conform to these standard proportions. You can take the liberty of shortening, lengthening, enlarging or distorting the head and the body, to suit the subject and the situation.

Making the minimum use of lines, note how a plain face has been developed into one with a funny expression.

Step–1   Step–2

Step–1   Step–2

Step–1   Step–2

4

Following the steps shown on page 4, draw the same faces in the circles given below. Colour the faces appropriately.

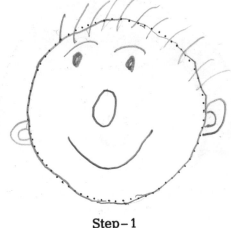

Step-1

Step-2

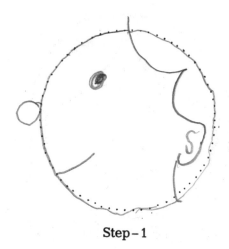

Step-1

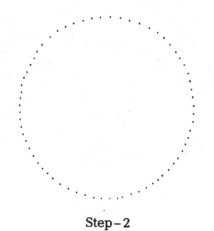

Step-2

Step-1

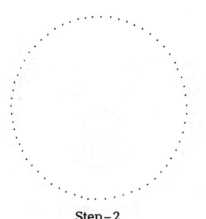

Step-2

LEARN TO DRAW CARTOONS

Observe these 6 faces carefully. Have you noticed how one basic face structure has been changed into various funny faces just by making minor changes?

Copy the faces shown on the left hand page, using the circles given below and then colour the faces.

A small line here, a small line there—
and a smiling face suddenly begins to cry!
Study these 6 faces carefully.

Smile

Big Smile

Laugh

Sad

Wonder

Cry

8

Using these circles, draw the different faces shown on page 8 and then colour them as you wish.

Observe these faces which have been drawn from the front and in profile. What a variety of expressions can be achieved!

Copy the full faces and profiles shown on the left hand page, using the circles given below. Colour them appropriately.

Once again, these characters have been drawn using a circle as a base. With the practice you have had so far, drawing these faces, should not be difficult.

Draw and paint faces similar to those shown on the left hand page, using the circles given below.

Wow! Here's a face created out of a mango shape and another one that uses the outline of an apple, as its base!

Try drawing them, using the given outlines and then have fun colouring them!

These two totally different characters have been created using two differently shaped fruits for the basic face structures.

What would you name them, Mr Prickly Pear and Mr Benny Banana? Draw and colour them.

The basic shape of a balloon has been used for these characters shown in full face and in three quarter profile. Try to draw them below and colour to complete the pictures.

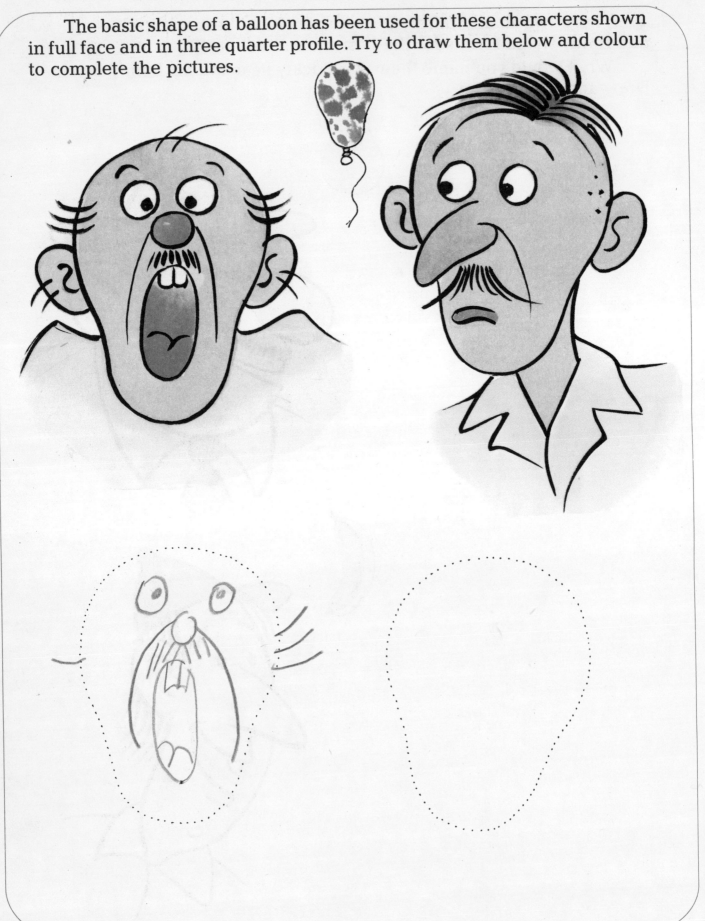

Mr Sad and Mr Happy, have been created using an egg shape. Try to sketch and colour them yourself, using the suggested outlines.

Draw Mr Calm and Mr Grumpy, using outlines given below and then colour them.

Make funny characters out of these fruit shapes and colour them. Use the above pictures as guidelines.

Working on a stick diagram is the most important, as well as the simplest way, to effectively sketch action figures. Drawn below are two figures, along with the basic stick figures. Now you try working on the third figure and then colour it.

Step-1   Step-2

Step-1   Step-2

Study how the second figure has been created from the first one. Work upon the third figure in a similar fashion and colour it.

Step – 1   Step – 2

Step – 1   Step – 2

See how step 1 has been converted into step 2. Now it is your turn to elaborate on the last two stick figures. Colour to complete.

Step–1

Step–2

Step–1

Step–2

22

The outlines of these faces have been drawn for you. All you have to do is to fill in the details so as not to lose the 'look' of the original character. Colour them neatly.

Provided below are some guidelines for sketching the three funny men. Complete the drawings and then colour them as you wish.

Here are a few starting point guidelines. Now you can draw and colour the faces.

Let us introduce you to Mr Oval. Study his different movements.
Can you visualise the basic stick figure in each drawing?

Here, the head positions have been marked for you. Draw the different actions of Mr Oval, imitating the figures shown on the left hand page.

Complete this action shot. Fill colour.

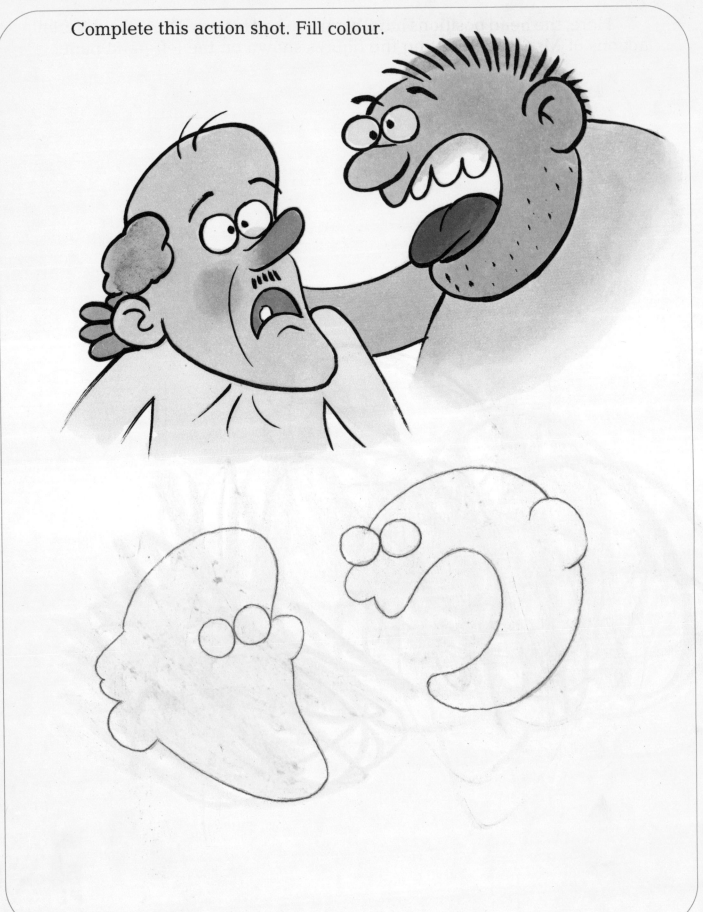

Fill in the details of the figures shown below and then paint your drawing neatly.

Shown below are examples that clearly illustrate a wide range of emotions that can be portrayed through animation. Observe these sketches carefully.

To make things easier, outlines have been given of the animal sketches on page 30. Complete the drawings using only the appropriate lines. Colour the sketches.

After studying the sketches given below, complete the drawings using the given outlines and then colour them.

Action! Action!

Complete the drawings without losing the sense of force and movement in the sketches. Colour them appropriately.

Using the given outlines on the right, complete these sketches of Prof. Jumbo and Magician Mumbo. Finish with colour.

Look again and you'll find that the 5 men and a woman drawn below, have the same basic face structure. Amazing, isn't it?

Making use of the guidelines, add those little extras that make each face look different. Try more for yourself. The possibilities are infinite!

35

Observe carefully and you'll find the digits 1 to 6 incorporated into the sketches below. So are the letters M and Z, as well as the words 'do job'.

Use the numbers and letters given below to construct funny faces as shown on page 36. Can you make some more of your own?

1   2   3

4   56

M   Z   dojob

Even inanimate objects do not escape the cartoonist's attention! He or she can bring magic to every object in sight.

Oh, no
Dad!

Following the animated drawings (figures) on the left hand page, try drawing your own version of them, using the given guidelines below.

The simplified form in step 1 has been elaborated upon to form this bawling infant in step 3.

Step-1

Step-2

Step-3

Draw him using the guidelines given in steps 2 and 3. Colour neatly.